Make friends with

Sheltie

The little pony with the big heart

Sheltie is the lovable little Shetland pony with a big personality. His best friend and owner is Emma, and together they have lots of exciting adventures.

Share Sheltie and Emma's adventures in

SHELTIE THE SHETLAND PONY
SHELTIE SAVES THE DAY
SHELTIE AND THE RUNAWAY
SHELTIE FINDS A FRIEND
SHELTIE TO THE RESCUE
SHELTIE IN DANGER
SHELTIE RIDES TO WIN
SHELTIE AND THE SADDLE MYSTERY
SHELTIE LEADS THE WAY
SHELTIE THE HERO
SHELTIE IN TROUBLE
SHELTIE AND THE STRAY
SHELTIE AND THE SNOW PONY
SHELTIE ON PARADE
SHELTIE FOR EVER

Peter Clover was born and went to school in London. He was a storyboard artist and illustrator before he began to put words to his pictures. He enjoys painting, travelling, cooking and keeping fit, and lives on the coast in Somerset.

Also by Peter Clover in Puffin

The Sheltie Series

1: SHELTIE THE SHETLAND PONY
2: SHELTIE SAVES THE DAY
3: SHELTIE AND THE RUNAWAY
4: SHELTIE FINDS A FRIEND
5: SHELTIE TO THE RESCUE
6: SHELTIE IN DANGER
7: SHELTIE RIDES TO WIN
8: SHELTIE AND THE SADDLE MYSTERY
9: SHELTIE LEADS THE WAY
10: SHELTIE THE HERO
11: SHELTIE IN TROUBLE
12: SHELTIE AND THE STRAY
13: SHELTIE AND THE SNOW PONY
14: SHELTIE ON PARADE
15: SHELTIE FOR EVER
16: SHELTIE ON PATROL
17: SHELTIE GOES TO SCHOOL
18: SHELTIE GALLOPS AHEAD
19: SHELTIE IN DOUBLE TROUBLE
20: SHELTIE IN PERIL
21: SHELTIE BY THE SEA
22: SHELTIE AND THE FOAL
23: SHELTIE RACES ON
24: SHELTIE AT THE FUNFAIR

Sheltie on Patrol

Peter Clover

For Brian, Anita and Dee

PUFFIN BOOKS

Published by the Penguin Group
Penguin Books Ltd, 80 Strand, London WC2R 0RL, England
Penguin Putnam Inc., 375 Hudson Street, New York, New York 10014, USA
Penguin Books Australia Ltd, 250 Camberwell Road, Camberwell, Victoria 3124, Australia
Penguin Books Canada Ltd, 10 Alcorn Avenue, Toronto, Ontario, Canada M4V 3B2
Penguin Books India (P) Ltd, 11 Community Centre, Panchsheel Park, New Delhi – 110 017, India
Penguin Books (NZ) Ltd, Cnr Rosedale and Airborne Roads, Albany, Auckland, New Zealand
Penguin Books (South Africa) (Pty) Ltd, 24 Sturdee Avenue, Rosebank 2196, South Africa

Penguin Books Ltd, Registered Offices: 80 Strand, London WC2R 0RL, England

www.penguin.com

First published 1999
4

Sheltie is a trade mark owned by Working Partners Ltd
Copyright © Working Partners Ltd, 1999
All rights reserved

Created by Working Partners Ltd, London W12 7QY

The moral right of the author has been asserted

Set in 14/22 Palatino

Made and printed in England by Clays Ltd, St Ives plc

British Library Cataloguing in Publication Data
A CIP catalogue record for this book is available from the British Library

ISBN 0–141–30451–0

Chapter One

It was Saturday morning and Emma was out in the paddock with Sheltie, her little Shetland pony. Emma sat on the wooden fence polishing Sheltie's bridle, which was cracked and worn in places, and didn't look as though it would last much longer.

Sheltie stood with his fuzzy chin resting on Emma's knee. He pushed his soft nose gently into her leg then blew all the air from his nostrils.

Sheltie's breath tickled Emma's hand as she worked on the bridle. She took the cloth and dusted the little pony's nose.

'That was a big sigh, Sheltie. Are you bored?' said Emma.

'A – tishoo!' Sheltie sneezed. Then he grabbed the cloth between his teeth and began shaking it to and fro.

'Oh, you want to play, do you?' Emma laughed. 'I guess you've had enough of standing still, haven't you?'

She slid off the fence and hooked the bridle over the rail.

Sheltie faced Emma with a cheeky look of mischief twinkling in his eyes. Emma was about to grab the cloth and start a game of tug-of-war when her mum suddenly called from the cottage.

'Emma! Come on, lunch is on the table.'

'Saved by the bell,' said Emma.

Sheltie dropped the cloth and blew a disappointed whicker as Emma hopped over the fence and raced up the garden path.

Inside the kitchen, everyone was about to start tucking into Mum's special pizza. Emma's little brother, Joshua, was busy picking all the bits of tomato off his slice, while Dad relaxed with his Saturday newspaper.

Dad scanned the pages then announced, 'This will interest you, Emma. "Reward given for information leading to the recovery of valuable prize pig. Telephone: Rilchester eight, six, two, five, six, five." You know what you're like with mysteries.' He added, 'I bet you could solve this one in five minutes flat.'

Mum glanced across the table and gave Dad a look.

'Now don't go encouraging her,' she smiled. 'Emma has enough excitement just looking after Sheltie. She certainly doesn't need to go traipsing around the countryside looking for a lost pig.'

'It's not lost,' said Dad. 'It says here that it was stolen.'

'Stolen,' repeated Emma. 'Who would want to steal a pig?'

'The same kind of people who steal ponies and sheep,' said Dad. 'Pigs probably fetch quite a bit at market sales. And this is a valuable *prize* pig.'

'It's probably worth quite a lot of money then. I could really use that reward,' said Emma. 'I could buy Sheltie a new bridle. His old one is almost falling to pieces.'

'Oh dear,' said Dad. 'Well I hope it lasts a bit longer. Things are a little tight at the moment, Emma, and new bridles can be quite expensive.'

'Perhaps a second-hand bridle wouldn't cost so much,' suggested Mum. 'There's a county show coming up and sometimes they have a farmers' market there too. We might be able to find Sheltie a cut-price bridle!'

'And I can save my pocket money,' said Emma brightly, 'and get a job to help out as well!'

Mum smiled and smoothed Emma's blonde hair.

'That's a sweet thought,' said Mum, 'but I expect we'll be able to manage the price of a bridle somehow.'

Emma gave Mum a hug. But she was still thinking about how she could get a job to help pay towards Sheltie's new bridle.

After lunch, Emma went back outside to the paddock. Sheltie was waiting eagerly for his afternoon ride. He had been cooped up in the paddock all morning while Emma had mucked out his field shelter and cleaned all his tack. Now he was raring to go somewhere.

Emma decided to ride Sheltie over to Horseshoe Pond and call in at the farm.

'Perhaps Mr Brown has some odd jobs we can help him with, Sheltie!'

The little pony shifted his feet and listened to Emma's voice as she spoke.

'We could help with the chickens or tidy up the barns,' she added. 'Let's go and see!'

After Emma and Sheltie had fed the ducks on Horseshoe Pond and sat there for a while on the little island, they went to visit the farmer.

Sheltie's little hoofs clattered on the grey flagstones as they trotted into the farmyard. Mr Brown was fixing his tractor and looked up as Sheltie blew a loud snort.

'Hello, Sheltie,' said the farmer, beaming a wide grin. 'Hello, Emma.' He wiped his forehead with the back of an oily hand and left a dirty streak above his eyebrows. 'I'm having a spot of bother getting Bessie here to start. You don't know anything

about tractors, do you?' he teased.

Sheltie blew a loud raspberry. This made Mr Brown laugh.

'Didn't think so,' he said.

'I wish I *did* know about tractors,' said Emma. 'I need a job so I can help pay towards Sheltie's new bridle. This old one's almost falling to pieces.'

'Oh dear,' said the farmer. 'We can't have that. Let me take a look.' He walked over to Sheltie and checked the little pony's bridle. While Mr Brown examined the cracked leather, Sheltie cheekily nibbled at the buttons on the farmer's waistcoat.

'Stop that, Sheltie!' said Emma.

Sheltie wasn't listening. He still held on to the button between his teeth.

'Sheltie!' warned Emma.

The little pony decided to let go.

'Fancy trying to eat Mr Brown's buttons, you naughty boy.'

'He's always full of mischief this one, isn't he?' grinned the farmer as he examined Sheltie's reins. Sheltie blinked and licked Mr Brown's hand.

'Well, the headset is fine,' said Mr Brown, 'but the reins are on the way out. The leather is all cracked and worn. I'll tell you what though, Emma, I've had some new sheep delivered to the West Acre – the farm meadow bordering the woods. It's an extra job for me, keeping an eye on them and counting them each evening.'

'I could do that,' interrupted Emma eagerly.

'Exactly,' said Mr Brown. 'If you could check on them for me every day after

10

school, and count them as well, then I'd say that's worth three pounds a week. What do you think?'

'Wow!' said Emma. Three pounds sounded like a lot of money for counting sheep. 'That's fantastic! We'll be your shepherds and watch the sheep. But I'll have to ask Mum and Dad first.'

'That's fine,' said the farmer. 'You go and ask your parents. Then when you come back I'll take you up to meet the new flock.'

Chapter Two

Emma raced back to the cottage as fast as Sheltie's trot would carry her. She burst into the kitchen brimming with excitement.

'I've got a job!' she cried. 'I've got a job! Sheltie and I are going to be shepherds.'

'What, both of you?' smiled Dad.

'Yes,' said Emma. 'We're going to watch over Mr Brown's new sheep in the West Acre and count them every day after

school. Will that be all right?' asked
Emma. 'I told Mr Brown I would have to
ask you first.'

'I should think that would be fine, don't
you, Mum?' said Dad.

'As long as it keeps you and Sheltie out
of mischief,' grinned Mum. 'You often go

riding past the West Acre after school anyway, don't you?'

'Yes. And now we'll be paid for it!' said Emma. 'Three pounds a week to go towards Sheltie's new bridle.'

'Well, I'd get back to the farm quickly if I were you, Emma,' teased Dad, 'in case someone else gets the job.'

Emma didn't have to be told twice. She turned on her heels, fastened the strap of her riding hat and flew out of the back door to fetch Sheltie.

Mr Brown walked with Emma and Sheltie up to the West Acre. Although Emma already knew where the meadow was, Mr Brown wanted to introduce them both to the new flock and make sure the sheep were all settling in.

'They're not ordinary sheep, as you'll see,' said the farmer. He ruffled Sheltie's mane as they walked across the lower meadow.

Sheltie sniffed at Mr Brown's jacket. The tweed material smelled of hay. Sheltie liked that smell. Then suddenly his ears pricked up and he took a deep sniff at the air around him. The little pony could smell something else now.

'Oh, look!' pointed Emma. 'There they are. I've never seen sheep like that before.'

Emma and Sheltie looked at the flock grazing in the meadow.

'They're called Jacob sheep,' said Mr Brown.

'They're all brown and white!' exclaimed Emma. 'And they've got horns.'

'That's what makes them different,' said

the farmer. 'They *all* have horns, even the ewes, but the young ones have two horns, while the adults have four. I'm raising them for their coloured fleeces,' he added.

Sheltie looked at the sheep through the wire fence and blew a loud snort. Then he watched them with his head tilted to one side.

'Sheltie can't decide if they're sheep or goats, can you, boy?' said Emma.

'He'll soon get used to them,' smiled Mr Brown. 'There should be twenty-five in here altogether.'

'I'll count them for you,' said Emma. She sat tall in Sheltie's saddle and started to count. As she did so, she pointed with her finger. And each time that Emma pointed, Sheltie scraped his hoof on the grass.

'I think Sheltie is counting too!' laughed the farmer.

Emma giggled. Sheltie was always copying things that Emma did.

'Twenty-three, twenty-four. Oh dear!' said Emma. She knitted her brows together and scanned the meadow. 'There are only twenty-four, Mr Brown. There's one missing.'

Sheltie blew a really deafening snort and shook out his mane so hard that all the birds took off from a nearby tree. The sudden noise also made one particularly fat sheep that was lying close to the fence struggle to its feet. Then, to Emma's surprise, she saw that it wasn't one sheep at all, but two sheep that had been lying next to each other.

'Oops, sorry,' said Emma. 'It's their patchy brown and white coats. When they're *that* close together it's hard to tell where one sheep ends and the next one begins. But it didn't fool Sheltie, though, did it?' she grinned.

'I don't think anyone could pull the wool over Sheltie's eyes!' laughed the farmer.

Emma listened carefully as Mr Brown

told her more about the job. Sheltie
seemed to listen too. He liked the farmer's
soft, calm voice. It almost sent him to
sleep.

'When you're counting the sheep,
Emma, keep a lookout for any that might
be limping or hobbling along. The West
Acre's quite a lumpy meadow and sheep
often sprain their ankles in dips and rabbit
holes. Also, watch out for any that are
coughing or looking generally unwell.'

'We will, won't we, Sheltie?'

The little pony opened his eyes
suddenly, then dipped his head and
nibbled at the tops of Mr Brown's wellies.

'You were dozing then, weren't you,
boy?' grinned Emma.

Sheltie looked embarrassed and blew a
quiet raspberry.

'There's a ditch on the far side, in front of that hedge,' added the farmer. 'If any of the flock are daft enough to fall in, then let me know straight away.'

Emma suddenly realized how responsible sheep-watching could be. She was determined that, with Sheltie's help, they would do a good job and be the best shepherds Mr Brown could ever want.

As the flock had already been counted that day and were all present and safe, Emma decided to take Sheltie for an afternoon ride through the woods before she went home for her tea. Mr Brown went back to the farm to mend his tractor.

'Look at all the leaves on the trees, Sheltie,' said Emma. 'They're already beginning to change colours. Soon all the branches will be bare.'

Sheltie looked up at the trees as they walked through the woods along Emma's favourite bridle path.

She liked this path because it led deep into the heart of the woods. Dry twigs and forest bark rustled and cracked beneath Sheltie's hoofs as he ambled along. They were in no hurry and both

Emma and Sheltie enjoyed the peaceful silence of the ride.

Sometimes Emma pretended that there was a secret castle hidden deep in the woods and that one day they would find it. But that afternoon there was no castle to be found. Instead, Emma and Sheltie discovered something much more exciting!

Chapter Three

Sheltie trotted along, stopped for a moment and began snuffling around in a pile of soft moss. Emma slackened the reins and let him root around for a bit. She knew that Sheltie had a knack for finding hidden treasures and was happy to let him have a moment to himself.

The little pony sniffed and snorted softly. Then, with his nose to the ground, Sheltie followed a trail over to a huge bush.

'*Now* what are you interested in?' said Emma.

Sheltie stared at the bush and pawed at the ground.

'Is there something in there, boy?'

Sheltie blew through his lips. He sounded like a faraway motorbike. Then he poked his head right into the bush!

'Sheltie! What are you doing?' Emma pulled his reins in and the little pony's head popped out again. In his mouth Sheltie held a small, flat piece of broken wood.

Emma leant across Sheltie's neck and gently took his find from his mouth. As she studied the piece of wood, Emma realized that it was part of some kind of nameplate. The letters 'PERK' were painted neatly on the flat wood in black brushwork.

'Perk,' said Emma. 'That's a funny name. I wonder what the rest of it would have been.' She slipped from the saddle and parted the bush with her hands.

As she did so, Sheltie took a mouthful of leaves and half the bush fell away. It wasn't a proper bush at all. It had been

broken off from somewhere else and used to cover what was lying behind it.

Sheltie stuck his head in again, next to Emma, and they both looked down at a pile of broken, smashed wood. There were also two wheels there which had been thrown on to the pile as well.

'It looks like the remains of a small trailer,' said Emma. 'I wonder who would have hidden that here. And why?'

Sheltie sneezed and made Emma jump. It was so quiet in that part of the wood.

She kept the piece of nameplate to take home and look at more carefully.

'Maybe we'll discover more about it, Sheltie,' she said, 'and find out who, or what, Perk was!'

Back at the cottage, after Emma had

finished her tea and settled Sheltie down for the night, she sat at the kitchen table. Dad's newspaper was spread out before her and Emma was busy drawing moustaches on all the faces with a felt-tip pen.

As she turned the pages, Emma found the article about the stolen pig. She followed the lines of print with her finger as she read to herself.

Suddenly she stopped and drew a big circle with the pen around a name in the story. 'PERKIN'.

'The stolen pig's called Perkin!' exclaimed Emma.

Dad looked over from the kitchen sink, where he was stacking dishes.

'Who's Perkin?' he asked.

'The pig,' said Emma. 'Perkin the pig!

The one that's been stolen.' She rushed upstairs to fetch the piece of nameplate. Then she told Mum and Dad all about Sheltie's discovery.

'It looks as though you may have come across something there,' said Dad.

'Trust you,' grinned Mum. 'If ever there's a mystery to solve, you can bet Emma is soon on the scent.'

'What should we do?' asked Emma.

'Well, whoever stole the pig has obviously tried to hide any evidence,' said Dad. 'The pig must have been stolen along with its trailer. Perkin is probably miles away by now, but I'm sure the police will be very interested in your discovery, Emma.'

'Tomorrow I'll telephone the number they put in the paper,' said Mum. 'I'm sure the pig's owners will be interested too!'

'Poor Perkin,' sighed Emma. 'I wonder what's happened to him.'

The next day was Emma and Sheltie's first day on official sheep patrol. Although Emma only had to check on the flock once a day at about five o'clock, she decided that if there *was* a pig-napper in the area, she would do extra little checks whenever she could.

'Whoever stole Perkin might be a sheep-napper too!' exclaimed Emma, as she finished her cereal.

'As long as you keep out of trouble,' warned Mum. 'And if you *do* see anything out of the ordinary, Emma,' she added, 'then you must tell us straight away.'

'*And* my boss,' said Emma. 'I shall tell
Mr Brown too.'

Dad smiled to himself. Emma always
thought of everything.

After breakfast, Mum telephoned
Perkin's owners. They were very
interested in what she told them and said
they would pass on all of Emma's

information themselves to the police.

Later, while Dad was preparing his special Sunday roast for lunch, Emma took Sheltie out on extra sheep patrol.

The West Acre wasn't far and it didn't take long to get there. Sheltie bounced along through the long grass of the middle field, tossing his mane in the bright sunshine.

When they got to the wire fence dividing the field from the West Acre, Sheltie stopped and stretched his neck over the top. Then he scratched his chin on the wire as Emma counted the flock.

This time, Emma was careful not to make any mistakes.

'Twenty-five!' cried Emma triumphantly.

Sheltie blew a snort in agreement and

pranced with his front legs padding the grass.

'They're all here,' said Emma. Then she looked to see if any of the flock were limping as Mr Brown had asked.

All the sheep were grazing peacefully and everything seemed fine. Emma decided to report back to Mr Brown. But first she thought another ride through the woods would be nice.

'We can check out Perkin's hidden trailer again, Sheltie, and see if we can find any more clues.'

Emma patted Sheltie's neck then turned him through a gate and towards the trees. Sheltie knew exactly where they were going and headed straight for the big bush in the heart of the woods.

But when they got there, Perkin's

smashed-up trailer was nowhere to be found. All remains of it had been mysteriously removed.

Chapter Four

'Someone's been here,' said Emma, 'and taken everything away.'

Sheltie sniffed at the ground then blew a puzzled snort. There were lots of muddy footprints around, but not one scrap of trailer to be found anywhere.

'Maybe the police have already been,' guessed Emma, 'or perhaps Perkin's owners have taken everything away. But then Mum only telephoned them a couple of hours ago! They must have been very quick.'

Sheltie harrumphed loudly. He raised his nose to the air and sniffed the wind. The little pony could smell smoke – and so could Emma.

'Someone's got a bonfire going,' she said.

Emma couldn't see anything, but the wind was blowing a definite bonfire smell from the woods.

'Come on, boy. Let's go and find out what's burning.'

Emma rode Sheltie even deeper into the woods. The trees grew thick and close together in places and Emma urged Sheltie to walk very quietly. His hoofs softly rustled the undergrowth as they made their way as silently as they could further into the woods.

Then, just up ahead, where the trees thinned out into a clearing, Emma saw something.

Sheltie stopped and Emma slid from the saddle. She held on to the reins to stop Sheltie from charging forward and stared at a big cattle wagon covered with a sheet of tarpaulin. The green canvas was pegged up at the front on two poles like a canopy.

Beneath the canopy were two wooden chairs and a table. The whole thing looked like a big tent with the cattle wagon hidden inside.

A few metres from the camp a bonfire burned slowly. Wispy spirals of smoke rose into the air and disappeared up through the branches of the overhanging trees.

Emma was very puzzled. There was no one around. The camp seemed deserted,

but someone must have built the fire quite recently. So why had they left all their things behind?

Sheltie made soft pony noises in the back of his throat and pushed his head against Emma's arm.

'I think we'd better go back and tell someone,' whispered Emma. Somehow the wagon camp seemed very suspicious.

Sheltie jangled his bit as Emma climbed back into the saddle. 'Come on, boy. Home.'

As they left the woods, Emma looked back over her shoulder.

At any minute she half expected someone to come running after them. But all was quiet.

Once out of the woods and into the open countryside, things were different.

Suddenly Emma felt really silly about letting an old wagon spook her. After all, it was only sitting there. But she was still going to tell Mr Brown about it all the same.

Back at the farm, Emma and Sheltie trotted round to the cow sheds looking for the farmer. Emma knocked on the open double doors and called out to Mr Brown, but there was no reply. Sheltie snorted a really loud whinney, but the farmer was not at home.

'He's probably gone out Sunday visiting,' said Emma, 'or maybe he's working in the fields somewhere. We'll have to come back later after we've done the proper sheep count at five o'clock.'

Emma looked at her watch. It was almost time for lunch anyway and suddenly she felt really hungry. She patted Sheltie's rump and headed back to the cottage.

Emma could smell Dad's special Sunday roast cooking the moment she entered the kitchen. The table was laid and Joshua sat patiently holding his knife and fork.

Over lunch, between mouthfuls of roast beef and crispy potatoes, Emma told her parents all about the missing trailer and the camouflaged wagon in the woods.

'Maybe Perkin's owners or the police have already been and taken the remains of the trailer away,' said Dad. 'I'll call PC Green at the station this afternoon. I think he might be interested to hear of any strangers camping out in the woods.'

'And I don't want you going anywhere near there again, Emma,' said Mum firmly.

'At least not until the police have been round,' she added, 'just in case there *is* something funny going on.'

'I won't,' promised Emma. But she was very interested to know why anyone would want to hide a cattle wagon in the heart of the woods.

When Dad spoke to PC Green, the policeman said he and PC McDonald would go over to the woods as soon as possible to investigate.

Emma couldn't help feeling excited about her discoveries and wanted to talk about them some more.

'It must have been a very small trailer,' she said. 'A tiny one, just big enough for a small pig.'

'It was,' said Mum. 'When I spoke to the owners earlier, they told me that it was made specially for Perkin. They used to take him to shows in it regularly. When Perkin was stolen from the show, the thieves just hooked up his trailer and drove it away.'

'With Perkin inside!' gasped Emma. 'Poor little pig.'

'Oink-oink,' giggled Joshua.

Dad laughed and ruffled Joshua's hair. Joshua was too young to understand about stealing.

After lunch, when everything was cleared away, Emma watched videos until it was time to take Sheltie out on sheep patrol.

'Don't forget to keep away from the woods,' reminded Mum.

'I won't,' said Emma.

It was very tempting to take Sheltie for a

quick trot through the woods, but Emma kept her promise to her mum and stayed on the other side of the track in the West Acre.

'Twenty-five, present and correct,' said Emma as she counted the sheep.

Sheltie pricked up his ears and sniffed the air. He seemed to be counting sheep too! But then Emma realized that Sheltie was more interested in the two figures ambling out of Bramble Woods than in the sheep.

Emma recognized them both straight away. It was PC Green and PC McDonald.

The two policemen walked out of the dark woods and into the afternoon sunshine. They saw Emma and Sheltie by the fence and gave a friendly wave. Emma trotted Sheltie over to find out what was happening.

'Hello,' said Emma eagerly. 'Have you been looking for the hidden wagon? Did you see it?'

Sheltie tossed his head and pushed his nose towards PC Green's hand. As the policeman stroked the pony's muzzle he told Emma what they had seen.

'Nothing!' he said. 'We found absolutely nothing. Whoever was camping in the woods has moved on without a trace.'

'There are no footprints.'

'And no tyre marks either,' added PC McDonald.

'But they *were* there,' insisted Emma. 'We saw them, didn't we, Sheltie?'

The little pony pawed at the ground with his hoof.

'Oh, we believe you, Emma,' said PC Green. 'It's just that there's no one there *now*. But we'll certainly be keeping a lookout for any strangers in the area. Especially ones with big cattle wagons.'

'And if you and Sheltie see anyone,' added PC McDonald, 'then you must tell us straight away.'

'Yes, we will,' promised Emma. 'Now that we're on sheep patrol we'll keep an eye on everything.'

The policeman gave Emma a wink. 'We

can always rely on you and Sheltie,' he smiled.

Emma gave Sheltie's neck a good hard pat. 'We won't let you down, will we, boy?'

Chapter Five

Once the two policemen had gone, Emma rode Sheltie straight back down to the farm. She found Mr Brown in one of the barns and told him all about the recent events.

The farmer listened very carefully. He was really pleased to have Emma and Sheltie working for him and keeping an eye on his sheep.

Mr Brown also had some news.

'There's a county show with a farmers' market coming to the next village at the end of the week,' he said. 'And I was wondering if you and Sheltie might like to tag along. You never know, we might find a second-hand bridle for the little fellow.'

'I'll have to ask Mum and Dad first,' said Emma, 'but we'd really like to come along.'

'I'll be taking the sheep trailer,' said the farmer, 'so I can give you and Sheltie a lift to the show. But I'm hoping to buy a ram at the market so you might have to follow the trailer home and ride Sheltie back to Little Applewood.'

'Oh, that's all right,' chirped Emma cheerfully. 'It's not very far, is it? Only a fifteen-minute ride past the school.'

'Well, don't forget to tell your parents about that part,' smiled the farmer. 'I don't

want them thinking I've left you all on
your own.'

When Emma got back home, she told her
parents about Mr Brown's offer. Mum and
Dad thought about it for a moment and
then agreed that it would be OK.

'After all,' said Dad, 'you go riding
much further when you take Sheltie out
over the moor.'

'And it's a straight road,' added Emma.
'It runs all the way from the market at
Chobham to Little Applewood.'

'Just make sure you stay close behind
Mr Brown,' warned Mum. 'And don't go
wandering off on your own at the market.'

'As if we would,' thought Emma.

The rest of the week passed very quickly.

Each day after school, Emma and Sheltie checked the sheep in the West Acre and then reported back to Mr Brown. They even rode through the woods a few times to see if the big wagon had turned up again, but there was no sign of it, or of anything else that was strange and out of the ordinary.

On Saturday morning, Mr Brown called in at the cottage to take Emma and Sheltie to the market. The farmer's open-top sheep trailer was just big enough for one small Shetland pony to stand comfortably inside.

'Look at Sheltie,' laughed Emma.

The little pony was standing in the trailer, as good as gold, with his fuzzy chin resting over the side.

Sheltie didn't know *exactly* where he was going, but he sensed that he was going somewhere, and that made him wonder if Emma was coming too! He looked over the side of the trailer and whinnied loudly.

'It's all right, boy,' said Emma. 'I'm still here. I'll be riding up front in the Land Rover with Mr Brown.'

Sheltie blew through his lips and settled down. Chobham wasn't very far. Emma knew they would be there in no time at all.

When they parked the Land Rover and wandered into the market square at Chobham, there was a livestock auction already in full swing.

It took Emma a few minutes to understand the auctioneer. He spoke so quickly in his sing-song voice that at first Emma thought he was speaking a foreign language. Then she began to understand and listened carefully as a little Exmoor pony was sold to the highest bidder.

Sheltie sniffed the air and took in the pony's scent. He wanted to trot over and make friends. There were so many interesting things to investigate all around him.

The market square was very busy and bustling with people. Sheltie could see sheep in wooden pens alongside pigs, goats and chickens in wire cages. He could smell more ponies too and his ears pricked up with excitement.

Emma had decided not to leave Sheltie tied up while she wandered around and held on tightly to his reins as she led him from stall to stall.

'Someone might try to sell you by mistake,' said Emma. 'That would be dreadful.'

Sheltie gave a gruff snort as if he agreed.

Mr Brown smiled and pointed to a nearby stall selling horse and pony tack.

'There you are, Emma,' he said. 'You have a browse around and see if they have any second-hand Sheltie-size bridles while

I go over there and look at the rams coming up for auction. Come and tell me if you find anything!'

Emma and Sheltie watched the farmer stroll across to the sheep pens, then Emma turned her attention to the tack stall.

'Do you need any help, dear?' asked the friendly stallholder. The woman smiled brightly and ran a hand through her short, ginger hair.

Emma looked at all the shiny new bridles hanging up at the back of the stall. Her hand felt for the small envelope tucked safely into her jacket pocket. Mum had given her some money, just in case.

'I *was* hoping you might have some second-hand bridles for sale,' said Emma.

As she spoke, Sheltie suddenly nosed his way into a box of assorted straps, reins, girths and other oddments.

'That's right,' laughed the stallholder, 'in that box of mixed tack. It's a right jumble, but you might just find what you're looking for!'

Sheltie grabbed the end of a lead rein and pulled it clean out of the box.

'No, Sheltie!' said Emma, 'we're looking for a bridle. Out of the way, let me take a look.'

But Sheltie wanted another go at looking. This time he pulled out a head collar.

'He's getting closer,' smiled the stallholder. 'Why don't I just tip the lot out and let you both have a good rummage?'

Emma and Sheltie sorted through the entire collection of oddments, but there was no used bridle to be found, only

brand-new ones hanging up at the back of
the stall – and they were very expensive.

Emma led Sheltie back over to the sheep
pens to look for Mr Brown. She found him
easily enough. Sheltie pushed his nose
into one of the farmer's pockets looking
for a treat.

'Now you keep out of there, Sheltie,' he
laughed. 'How can I pay for this ram I've
just bought if you keep messing about?'

'I'll take him over to look at the sale animals and keep him out of your way,' grinned Emma.

She wandered back with Sheltie over to the enclosure where more livestock were about to be auctioned.

Chapter Six

Emma saw a giant carthorse, some small shaggy ponies, a nosy goat and six squealing piglets. The piglets made Emma think of Perkin.

'I wonder if poor Perkin will ever be brought to market and sold,' she thought.

Then Emma saw a thin, sad-looking donkey tethered to a post with a 'FOR SALE' sign around its neck. The black donkey was very bony and its neck and haunches were sunken.

Emma could hear a sighing breath each time its thin flanks rose and fell. The poor thing looked so sad. Emma tried to imagine how it would look, well fed and cared for.

Sheltie looked at the donkey too, then cocked his head to one side and whickered softly. Sheltie must have thought it was his donkey-friend Mudlark. The black donkey turned its face towards Sheltie and blinked its sad eyes.

Emma stroked the thin neck and bristly mane. Then she smoothed her hand across its shoulders and down the donkey's legs. They seemed very hot. Emma knew that hot legs usually meant a pony or donkey was sickly – Mr Thorne the vet had told her that.

Emma ran her hand over the donkey's knees. The hairs there felt very strange and rough, like a paintbrush that hadn't been washed out properly.

Emma looked again more closely. Then she took out a white handkerchief from her pocket and rubbed the donkey's leg. When she looked at the hanky in her hand it was black. Not black from dirt, but black from some kind of dye or paint.

Suddenly, Emma realized that for some reason this donkey had been disguised.

She checked all of its legs. They had all been painted black from the knee down. Its legs were really white.

Emma's stomach turned a somersault.

'I bet this donkey's been stolen, Sheltie,' she whispered. '*And* it's sickly too. We'd better go and tell Mr Brown. He'll know what to do.'

Emma was in such a rush to help the poor animal that, as she turned, she bumped right into two men who were standing nearby. It was quite a crash too. Sheltie even managed to tread on the feet of one of them.

'Ow! Watch it!' he cried out gruffly. 'What's the big hurry?'

Sheltie blew a noisy raspberry.

Emma's face flushed hot with embarrassment. She was so surprised by the men that she blurted out her suspicions about the donkey in one long, hurried breath.

'I'm sure this donkey is stolen and it's sickly and not very well and its legs have been painted black to disguise it and I've got to tell the police . . .'

Then, to Emma's amazement, the two men took off and disappeared into the crowd without another word.

Emma and Sheltie waited with the donkey. Emma thought the two men had gone to call the police. But after ten minutes, when they didn't come back, she decided to go and tell Mr Brown.

Mr Brown was just getting ready to lead his ram to the trailer when Emma and Sheltie turned up. The ram seemed quite docile and stood quietly wearing a rope halter.

Emma quickly told the farmer what had happened and how she suspected that the donkey had been stolen.

Mr Brown listened carefully. 'I know that you're not one for making up stories, Emma,' he said, 'so let's go and take a look.'

He also knew that if Emma thought an animal was sick, she was probably right!

Mr Brown settled the ram safely into his trailer and then went to check on Emma's story. But by the time they got back to the auction enclosure the little donkey had gone.

Emma asked some people standing nearby if they had seen anything.

'There were two men,' said a young couple. 'One was tall and thin with a scar on his face. The other was shorter and fatter with a beard. They came and quickly bustled the donkey away into a big grey cattle wagon.'

These men fitted Emma's description exactly.

'Don't worry, Emma,' said Mr Brown. 'As soon as we get back home I'll ring the police and warn them that there's something fishy going on. If that donkey *was* stolen, I'm sure the police will have a record of it.'

Emma couldn't get Sheltie away from the market quickly enough. She didn't like the idea of stolen animals turning up and being sold – especially when the real owners were out there somewhere, probably feeling really miserable, not knowing what had happened to their pets and animals.

Emma couldn't imagine what it would feel like if Sheltie was stolen. It was too horrible to think about.

Sheltie was eager to be on the move again as well. He didn't like those two nasty men either and wanted to be back in his paddock as quickly as possible.

It wouldn't take long to reach the village, but this time Emma had to ride Sheltie along behind Mr Brown's trailer, so going back would take a little longer than coming.

Sheltie could see the top of the ram's head in the open trailer. As he trotted along behind, the little pony blew a loud whicker and the ram answered with a deep 'Baah!'

This made Emma laugh to herself. It was as if Sheltie seemed to know that the ram was coming to live in Little Applewood. It was typical of her pony to start making friends straight away.

They covered the distance back to the village in half an hour. As they crossed the stone bridge that led the way past her cottage and down to the farm, Emma urged Sheltie on and overtook the Land Rover at a fast canter.

Mr Brown wound down his window.

'What's the hurry, Emma?' he laughed. 'It's not a race.'

Emma gave the farmer her biggest grin and pointed to her wristwatch.

'Time for sheep patrol,' she answered. 'If you carry on down the lane to the farm, I can take Sheltie the back way, across and round through Bramble Woods, to check the flock in the West Acre.'

'Good idea,' smiled Mr Brown. He was pleased that Emma was taking her job so seriously. 'I'll settle Rambo in one of the barns for his first night while you take Sheltie on patrol.'

The farmer waved as Emma turned her

little Shetland pony around and took a
short cut back across the fields to Bramble
Woods and the meadow.

Chapter Seven

Emma and Sheltie's trek through the woods to the West Acre was beautiful.

The afternoon sun was sitting low in the sky and sending the last of its soft golden rays slanting through the trees to dapple their path. All around them the rough grass was alive with the drone of bees and the whirr of insects.

Sheltie took in a deep breath and blew a contented snort.

'It's great, isn't it, boy?' agreed Emma.

Beyond the woods, Mr Brown's sheep grazed peacefully in the shimmering meadow of the West Acre.

Then suddenly, Sheltie sensed that something was wrong. The little pony stopped in his tracks. Emma felt it too! All the fine hairs on the back of her neck stood on end.

They were just at the very edge of the woods, only a few steps away from the rough track which ran between the woods and the fenced meadow. Hidden in the shadows thrown by the last row of trees, Emma drew in her breath and sat on Sheltie as still as a statue.

In front of them she saw a grey cattle wagon. It was the same one she had seen before, hidden in the woods, only this time, the wagon had been used to knock down the wire fence and two men were lowering a ramp into the meadow. Emma recognized them both straight away. One was tall and thin with a scar on his face. The other was shorter and fatter with a beard.

'They're the two men from the market,' whispered Emma, 'and they're about to steal Mr Brown's sheep!'

Emma and Sheltie watched as both men waved their arms up and down and began herding the flock towards the wagon.

Sheltie flattened his ears and grumbled in his throat with a low whicker.

'Shh, boy,' whispered Emma. She patted Sheltie's neck softly. 'What are we going to do?'

Sheltie pawed at the ground with his

hoof and shook his head up and down. He seemed to be telling Emma that they should make a quick dash across the meadow and warn Mr Brown before it was too late.

Emma knew that the quickest way to the farm was across the meadow, but there was no time to open the gate. That meant they had to ride through the broken fence and right past the wagon. And those two men looked gruff and mean.

'I don't fancy our chances,' whispered Emma. Her heart was thumping so hard that she thought the men would hear it at any minute, even above the nervous bleating of the sheep as they clattered up the ramp into the back of the wagon.

'Perhaps we should just go for it though,' thought Emma, 'and risk being caught.' She loosened her grip on the reins and, as she urged Sheltie forward, he took matters into his own hoofs.

Soon Sheltie was galloping towards the gap and down into the meadow with his mane and tail flying wildly.

'Keep going, Sheltie,' thought Emma. 'We just might be able to make it and get down to the farm in time to warn Mr Brown.'

But just at that moment, the men spun round and saw them. The tall, thin one was very fast indeed – suddenly he was running towards them across Sheltie's path. Emma squeezed with her legs and urged Sheltie to go even faster, but Sheltie was going as fast as he could.

The man was now standing directly in front of them, blocking their way, and, as Sheltie swerved to avoid a crash, the man reached out and grabbed the little pony's reins.

'Gotcha!' he sneered.

Emma's heart missed a beat. But then she realized that the man hadn't *got* them at all!

He had grabbed the reins all right, but the leather was old and worn and had snapped in his grasp.

The man fell backwards and landed with a thump. His mouth hung open in surprise as he watched Emma and Sheltie bolt off across the meadow and down towards the farm.

Emma hung on tightly to Sheltie's mane as he thundered over the bumpy ground.

The broken reins flew out to the sides like wild streamers.

The men's shouts rang in Emma's ears, but she didn't dare look back. The farm loomed closer and closer with each galloping stride.

Then they were hurtling into the farmyard and Emma grabbed the broken reins and pulled Sheltie to a halt. She flung herself from the saddle and ran to the barns.

'Mr Brown! Mr Brown! Come quickly!' she yelled to the farmer from the doorway. 'Rustlers are taking the sheep.'

Sheltie stuck his nose round the door and blew a loud snort of urgency.

Mr Brown had just settled Rambo into his pen. One look at Emma and wild-eyed Sheltie was enough to tell him that he had to move fast.

Emma and Sheltie followed Mr Brown at a run to the house and watched him go inside to telephone the police. Then, with a look of disbelief, he came straight out again and said to Emma, 'The phone's dead!'

Sheltie blew a snort and looked up at the telephone cable dangling from the wall above the door.

'They must have been here earlier, Emma,' said the farmer. 'Look! They've cut the wires.'

Emma could clearly see the two halves of the telephone cable hanging from the wall.

Then Mr Brown asked Emma a strange question.

'When you saw the cattle wagon backing into the meadow, which way was it facing?'

Emma looked puzzled. Why was Mr Brown worrying about which way the wagon was facing when his sheep were being stolen?

'Think carefully, Emma. It's very important,' he said.

Emma thought hard.

'It was facing *down* the track, away from the village,' said Emma.

'Are you sure?'

Sheltie blew a shrill whinney.

'Positive,' answered Emma.

'Right,' said the farmer. 'I'll take the tractor and cut around the fields to block their escape route to the main road. Do you think you could ride Sheltie at a fast gallop back along the lane to the police house in the village and raise the alarm?'

Mr Brown didn't have to ask twice.

Within seconds Emma was back in the saddle and urging Sheltie to race as fast as he could along the home lane. She held on tightly to the broken reins, one in each hand.

It seemed strange galloping right past her own cottage without stopping to tell Mum or Dad, but Emma knew that time was important. She had to alert the police as quickly as possible.

Sheltie's hoofs drummed the ground as they flew along like the wind. His little legs were moving so fast that you could hardly see them.

'Come on, Sheltie,' yelled Emma. 'Keep going, we're almost there.'

The pony's mane and tail streamed out behind him as they reached the little stone bridge at the end of the lane.

79

A quick clattering of hoofs on the cobbles and they were over the stream and galloping down into the village. The police house was the first cottage on the left.

Emma hoped that PC Green would be at home. If he wasn't, they would have to ride right through the village to the police station a little further on.

Emma pulled Sheltie up outside PC Green's house. The little pony was puffing and blowing hard. It had been *some* race. Sheltie cleared his nostrils with a puffing snort and Emma clapped his neck.

'Well done, boy. Well done.' Then she dismounted and rushed to knock on the door.

'Come on. Come on.' Emma was

hopping from one foot to the other.

'Come on. Where are you?'

She knocked again, then breathed a sigh of relief as the door swung open.

Chapter Eight

'Hello! It's Emma, isn't it?' smiled Mrs Green.

Emma's face dropped. 'Is PC Green there?' she almost shouted. 'It's an emergency!'

The sound of tyres crunching to a halt on gravel made Emma spin round. Sheltie was already peering through the window of PC Green's Range Rover and steaming up the windscreen with his hot breath.

Emma rushed over to the car. She was breathless and excited, but managed to get her story out to the two policemen.

'And you've ridden all the way here on Sheltie?' said PC McDonald.

Sheltie nodded his head and whickered friskily. He pawed at the ground and seemed eager to get going again.

'Mr Brown has taken his tractor to block the rustlers' escape on to the main road, but *please* hurry,' pleaded Emma. 'He might be in trouble.'

Suddenly PC Green jumped to it. 'The quickest way there is to take a short cut across the lower fields,' he said. Then turned to Emma and asked, 'Do you think you could race ahead on Sheltie and open the big five-bar gate for us?'

Emma was up on Sheltie and heading

for the gate before the police car had even pulled away from the kerb.

Sheltie blew an impatient harrumph as PC Green steered the Range Rover through the gate and into the field. He seemed to be saying, 'Come on, hurry up! Can't you go any faster?'

Emma watched as the police car tore across the grass to the West Acre meadow.

'Come on, boy,' yelled Emma, 'let's go.' She forgot the reins and grabbed a handful of Sheltie's mane. 'We don't want to miss this. Pony patrol, charge!'

Although he was small, Sheltie was fast. But no matter how quickly he galloped he couldn't keep up with the police car. By the time they arrived at the scene of the crime, it was nearly all over.

Mr Brown was standing by his tractor
and shaking his fist at the rustlers as the
two policemen handcuffed them and led
them away to the police car.

Emma could see that all the tractor
windows had been smashed. Mr Brown
seemed unhurt.

'The police must have got there just in
the nick of time,' said Emma.

She rode up on Sheltie as the farmer
lowered the wagon's ramp and let the
sheep back out into the meadow.

The flock were making a terrible din and Emma was busy counting horns to make sure there were twenty-five sheep present and correct.

Then, to everyone's surprise, a little black donkey flew out of the wagon and clattered down the ramp into the meadow. It ran straight up to Sheltie and rubbed noses with the little pony.

'Where on earth did *he* come from!' said Mr Brown, scratching his head.

'It's the donkey we told you about,' cried Emma. 'It must have been stolen after all. Those men were trying to sell it at the market – that's why they ran away when I mentioned the police.'

'Well done, Emma,' smiled the farmer. 'You're a proper little detective, aren't you?'

Then, just as Mr Brown was about to put up the ramp, Sheltie started to kick up a terrible fuss. He cantered over to the back of the wagon and began to blow and snort and paw the ground with his hoof.

'What's the matter, boy?' asked Emma.

Sheltie seemed determined that someone should take another look inside the wagon.

He raised his hoof high and scraped at the end of the ramp.

'I think Sheltie's trying to tell us something,' said Emma.

Mr Brown looked puzzled, but listened to what Emma was saying. Slowly, he lowered the ramp again. Then cautiously he climbed up inside the wagon.

Emma and Sheltie waited patiently. Suddenly, there was a yell, followed by a shrill squealing sound coming from inside the wagon. It was very loud. Sheltie's ears pricked up straight away. He always knew when another animal was frightened and that was exactly what this noise sounded like.

Seconds later, Mr Brown came staggering out of the wagon under the weight of a very fat pig. The farmer cradled the squirming pig in his arms as he tottered down the ramp.

'It's Perkin!' cried Emma. 'It's Perkin, the missing prize pig.'

PC Green left his partner in charge of the two rustlers and came to look at the struggling pig. There was a number tattooed inside its ear.

'If this *is* Perkin,' he said, 'then I happen to know that there is a very handsome reward for finding him.'

'Well, that reward will go to Emma,' huffed Mr Brown as he struggled to keep hold of the wriggling pig. 'And if it's not enough to buy Sheltie that new bridle,' he added, 'then I'll put up the rest for saving my sheep.'

Sheltie tossed his head and the broken reins dangled from his bit.

'But it's a good job that old leather *did* break,' said Emma, 'otherwise those nasty men would have caught us. If Sheltie's reins hadn't snapped when they did, who knows what would have happened!'

Sheltie blew a loud whistling snort through his nostrils as if to say, 'It would take more than the likes of those two to catch me!' Then he trotted over to make friends with the donkey and to help Mr Brown calm down the squealing pig.

If you like making friends, fun, excitement and adventure, then you'll love

The little pony with the big heart!

Sheltie is the lovable little Shetland pony with a big personality. He is cheeky, full of fun and has a heart of gold. His owner, Emma, knew that she and Sheltie would be best friends as soon as she saw him. She could tell that he thought so too by the way his brown eyes twinkled beneath his big, bushy mane. When Emma, her mum and dad and little brother, Joshua, first moved to Little Applewood, she thought that she might not like living there. But life is never dull with Sheltie around. He is full of mischief and he and Emma have lots of exciting adventures together.

Share Sheltie and Emma's adventures in:

SHELTIE IN TROUBLE
SHELTIE AND THE STRAY
SHELTIE AND THE SNOW PONY
SHELTIE ON PARADE
SHELTIE FOR EVER